Basic Skills

HANDWRITING

for 6 – 7 year olds

Contents

Unit 1   Introducing joined writing

Unit 2   Introducing the first join

Unit 3   Practising the first join

Unit 4   Introducing the second join

Unit 5   Practising the second join

Unit 6   Handwriting patterns

Progress check 1

Unit 7   Introducing the third join

Unit 8   Practising the third join

Unit 9   Introducing the fourth join

Unit 10   Practising the fourth join

Unit 11   Break letters

Unit 12   Handwriting practice

Progress check 2

Extra practice

Record sheet

Louis Fidge

Introducing joined writing

 **FOCUS**

In this book you will be learning
how to do **joined writing** like this:

A quick brown fox
jumps over the lazy dog.

 TRY THESE

In joined writing these two letters look different.
Practise writing them.

 and

f f f

k k k

MORE PRACTICE

Complete the word under each picture with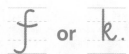

 king

__rog

__ettle

__lag

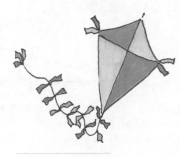

__ite

__ish

✓ CHECK UP

Find and circle the letters f and k.

a g (k) s u h f m z k l t

q f d b k r n l f k x y k f

Introducing the first join

 **FOCUS**

There are four main joins in handwriting.
This is an example of the **first join**.
Write over the word in different colours.

 TRY THESE

Practise writing these words.

 pin   p—   p—   p—   p—

 pan   p—   p—   p—   p—

 pen   p—   p—   p—   p—

Unit 2

Tick ☑ the correct word. Copy the word twice.

cup ☑ cap ☐   cup   cup

lap ☐ lip ☐

pip ☐ pup ☐

hem ☐ ham ☐

sup ☐ sun ☐

CHECK UP

Make up words using each of these letters.

c
m → an → can _____ _____
p

Practising the first join

Here are some more letter patterns and words that contain the first join.

TRY THESE

Copy and practise these letter patterns.

ag   ag

ad   ad

ar   ar

ug   ug

um   um

MORE PRACTICE

Copy the words carefully.

my bun

my bag

my dad

my mum

 ✓ CHECK UP

Copy these words.

lag   bar   mad   bug   hum   sun

Introducing the second join

FOCUS

This is an example of the **second join**.
Write over the word in different colours.

 TRY THESE

Copy these letter patterns and words.

 ill   ill   ·   ·   ·

hill   hill   ·   ·

ell   ell   ·   ·   ·

bell   bell   ·   ·

MORE PRACTICE

Copy these rhymes carefully.

Ding dong dell.

Pussy's in the well.

Jack and Jill went up the hill.

CHECK UP

Make some words using *ill*, *ell*, *all*.

b ill   b ____   b ____

t ____   t ____   t ____

Practising the second join

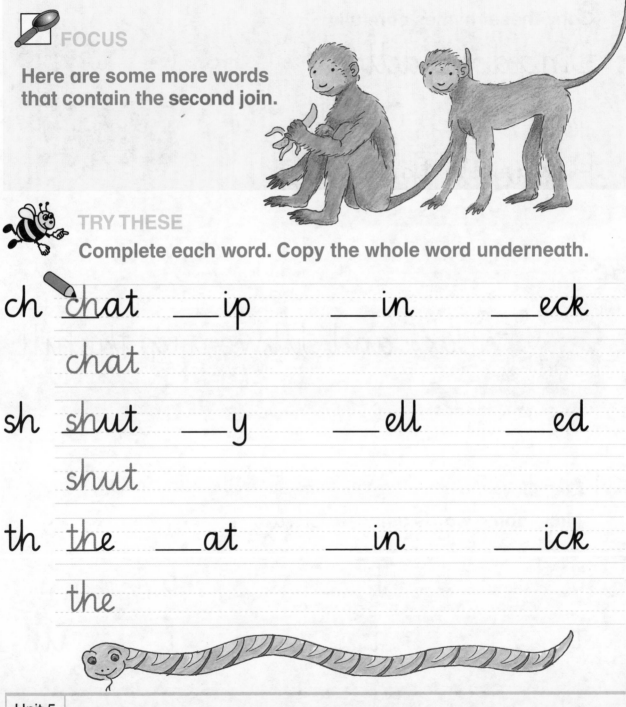

FOCUS

Here are some more words
that contain the **second join**.

TRY THESE

Complete each word. Copy the whole word underneath.

ch   chat   __ip   __in   __eck

chat

sh   shut   __y   __ell   __ed

shut

th   the   __at   __in   __ick

the

MORE PRACTICE

Copy the sentences carefully.

I like to eat chips.

I like thick sandwiches.

I like a bubble bath.

☑ CHECK UP

Write the correct word next to each picture.

path

sheep

chimp

path

Handwriting patterns

The patterns on these pages will help you to form and join letters more easily.

Trace over the patterns in different colours. Finish the lines of patterns.

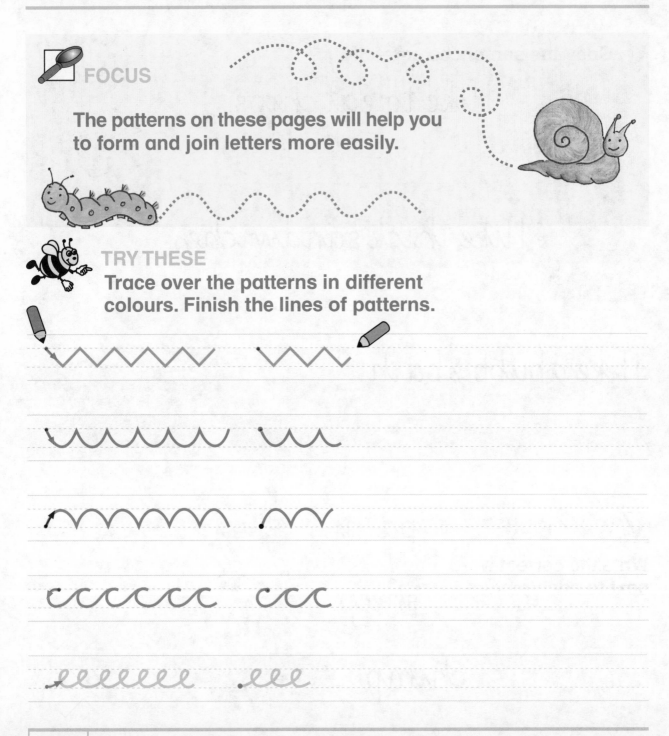

MORE PRACTICE
Copy these patterns.

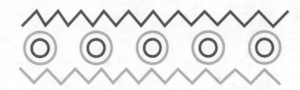

 CHECK UP
Colour in this pattern neatly.

Unit 6

Practise these letters.

f f   k k

Copy these letter patterns and words.

in   ig   im   up   ud

tin   dig   him   cup   mud

eg   leg   am   jam

Copy the letter patterns and words.

ill till

uck duck

sh sheep

ch chimp

Trace over each pattern. Now make a pattern of your own.

Introducing the third join

FOCUS

This is an example of the **third join**.
Write over the letters in different colours.

TRY THESE

Copy and practise these letter patterns.

oa   oa   ·   ·   ·   ·

og   og   ·   ·   ·   ·

ow   ow   ·   ·   ·   ·

ock   ock   ·   ·   ·   ·

ox   ox   ·   ·   ·   ·

MORE PRACTICE
Copy the words carefully.

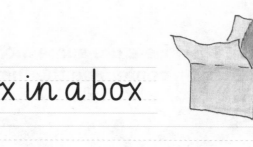

a fox in a box

a

a dog in a fog

a crow in the snow

a goat in a boat

✓ CHECK UP
Complete these words with og, ox, ow **or** ock.

j_____   f_____   gr_____   s_____

Practising the third join

 **FOCUS** Here are some more letter patterns and words containing the third join.

 TRY THESE Copy these letter patterns and words.

fi *fi*

fire *fire*

we *we*

web *web*

va *va*

van *van*

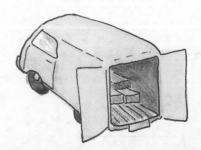

Unit 8

MORE PRACTICE

Write these beside the correct pictures.

a wiggly worm   five fat frogs

a very old vulture

☑ **CHECK UP**

Copy these words.

good   cars   went   five

Introducing the fourth join

 **FOCUS**

This is an example of the fourth join.
Write over the letters in different colours.

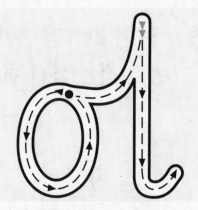

 TRY THESE

Copy and practise these letter patterns and words.

oll oll

doll doll

ole ole

mole mole

Unit 9

MORE PRACTICE

Copy these sentences carefully.

I am a mole.

I am a doll.

I am an old whale.

CHECK UP

Here are some more sentences for you to copy.

I am a mole. I live in a hole.

Unit 9

Practising the fourth join

FOCUS

Here are some more letter patterns that contain the fourth join.

TRY THESE

Copy these letter patterns.

fl *fl*

ft *ft*

rl *rl*

rk *rk*

wl *wl*

MORE PRACTICE

Write these under the correct picture.

bark and growl

lift a log   a girl with curls

✓ CHECK UP

Use these letters to complete the words.

wl   rl   ft   rk

gi____   pa____   o____   lo____

Break letters

FOCUS

We never make a join after any of these letters:

b g j p q x y z

TRY THESE   Copy these words carefully.

boy   girl   jam   pen

boy

queen   foxes   yam   zip

MORE PRACTICE

Here are some more words for you to copy.

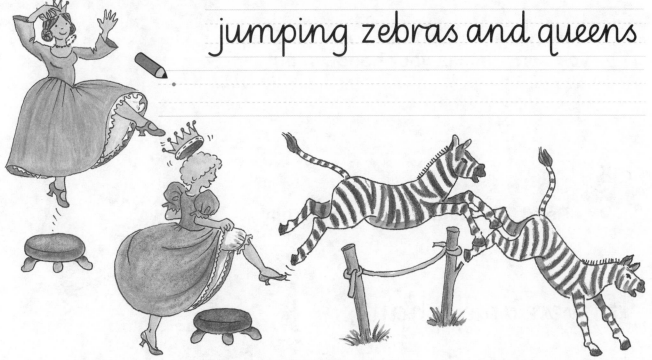

jumping zebras and queens

yellow and green boxes

✓ CHECK UP

Find and circle all the break letters.

a (b) c d e f g h i j k l m

n o p q r s t u v w x y z

Handwriting practice

FOCUS

Now you have learnt to do all the joins,
you can practise your handwriting!

TRY THESE

Read this rhyme. Write it carefully.

If I were an elephant,

big and strong,

I'd wave my trunk and walk along.

If

MORE PRACTICE
Copy this rhyme carefully.

Rain on the house-top and on the tree.

Rain on the grass but not on me!

R

 CHECK UP This sentence contains every letter of the alphabet.

A quick brown fox

jumps over the lazy dog.

do not disturb

Progress check 2

Copy these letter patterns and words.

op   hop   ws   cows   fa   fat

old   cold   of   often   wl   owl

bath   gate   jump   party

queen   boxes   yellow   zoo

Copy this poem carefully.

The elephant is big and strong,

His ears are large, his trunk is long.

He walks around with heavy tread,

His keeper walking at his head.

Extra practice

Copy these rhymes in your best handwriting.

I am a spider.

I like to crawl

In my web

And on your wall.

Down in the grass, curled in a heap,

Lies a fat snake, fast asleep.

When he hears the grasses blow,

He moves his body to and fro.

Record sheet

How easy did you find it?

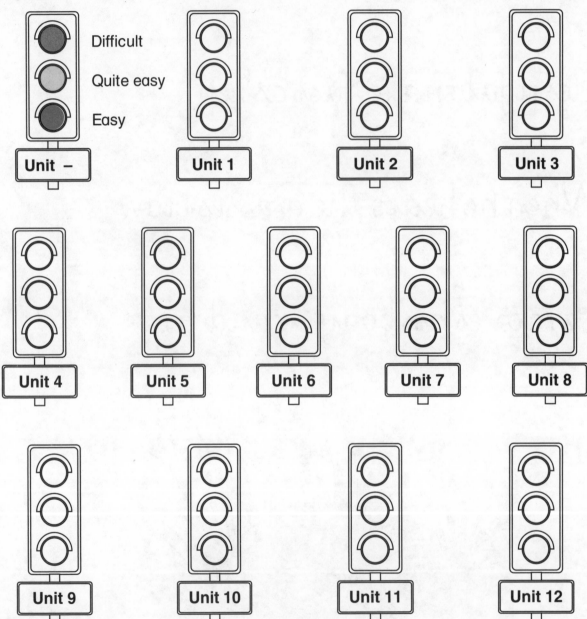